# Garfield hangs out

### BY: JIM DAVIS

**BALLANTINE BOOKS · NEW YORK**

Library of Congress Catalog Card Number: 89-92608

ISBN: 0-345-36835-5

Manufactured in the United States of America

First Edition: October 1990

10  9  8  7  6  5  4  3  2  1

# PET PICKS & PANS

**PET EXPERT GARFIELD ON CATS AND THEIR COMPETITION**

**RABBITS:** BUY TWO CHOCOLATE ONES AND HOPE THEY MULTIPLY.

**HAMSTERS:** BIG DUMB COUSINS OF MICE.

**GOLDFISH:** NEAT, QUIET, DON'T NEED WALKING, AND IN A PINCH THEY MAKE A TASTY HORS D'OEUVRE.

**SPIDERS:** THAT'S NOT A PET; THAT'S A NIGHTMARE.

**MICE:** SURE, THEY'RE CUTE, BUT THEY ONLY LOVE YOU FOR YOUR CHEESE.

**BOA CONSTRICTORS:** RIGHT. NOTHING LIKE A PET THAT WILL HUG YOU, THEN EAT YOU.

**PARROTS:** PRETTY BIRDS. A GOOD ACCESSORY WITH AN EYE PATCH AND PEG LEG.

**DOGS:** LOVING, LOYAL, OBEDIENT, AND BREATH THAT WOULD STUN A YAK.

**CATS:** NATURE'S MOST PERFECT PET. NEED I SAY MORE?

3-1

3-2

POIT

JIM DAVIS 3-13

SNIP!

3-14

WHAP!

JIM DAVIS

SQUISH

JIM DAVIS

3-17

WHAP!

JIM DAVIS 3-18

© 1989 United Feature Syndicate, Inc.

3-19

JIM DAVIS

4-2 JIM DAVIS

© 1989 United Feature Syndicate, Inc.

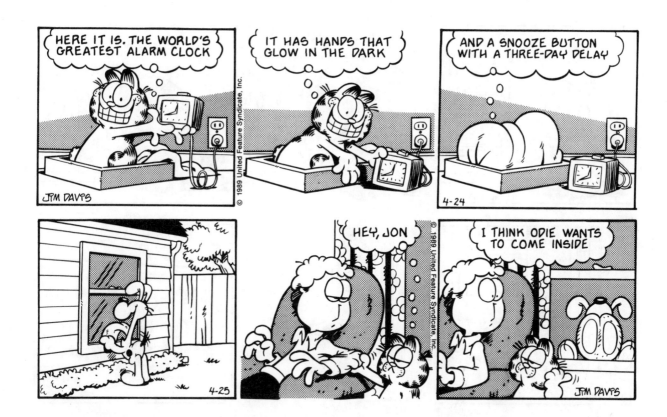

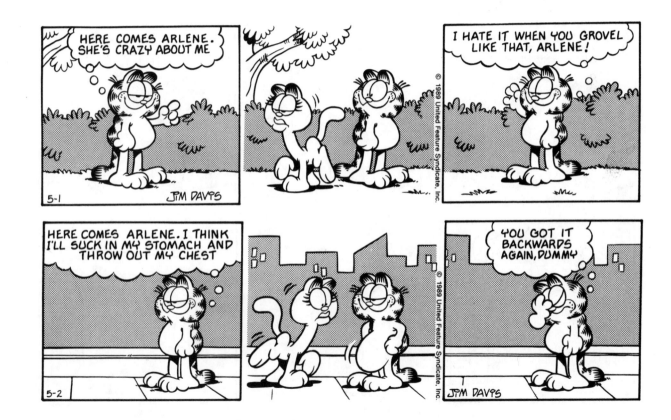

# GARFIELD

YOU FORGOT TO PUT CREAMED CORN ON THE GROCERY LIST, OPIECUS

GARFIELD'S CAT PRIMER

WHY CATS ARE LAZY...

GARFIELD

CAT'S POINT OF VIEW

© 1989 United Feature Syndicate, Inc.

WHY CATS NEED HELP.

CAT'S POINT OF VIEW

WHY CATS HATE DOGS...

CAT'S POINT OF VIEW

JIM DAVIS   5-14

AND WHY CATS ARE VAIN...

A CAT'S FAVORITE VIEW

WOW! JELLY BEANS!
I LOVE JELLY BEANS!

© 1989 United Feature Syndicate, Inc.

JIM DAVIS    5-21

SLURP!

ODIE LEFT HIS BRAIN TO SCIENCE

5-26

© 1989 United Feature Syndicate, Inc.

AND THEY MADE AN EARLY WITHDRAWAL

JIM DAVIS

Z

© 1989 United Feature Syndicate, Inc.

JIM DAVIS

5-27

Z

I'M EXHAUSTED!

I GUESS I OVERDID IT

THAT'S THE LAST TIME I TAKE THREE NAPS IN A ROW WITHOUT A BREAK

5-29

HELLO? DEBBIE, MY SWEET?

YOU FAT GREEDY PIG! I OUGHTA SHAVE YOU BALD AND PUT YOU OUT IN THE COLD

5-30

HELLO?

CLICK

I CAN'T BELIEVE I'LL BE ELEVEN YEARS OLD TOMORROW

OH, WELL, TIME TO GET THESE OLD BONES OUT OF BED

OKAY, TOES

CRACK
CRACK 'CRACK
CRACK 'CRACK
CRACK

OKAY, KNEES. OKAY, ARMS

CRACK CRACK
CRACK CRACK

OKAY, KNUCKLES. OKAY, NECK

CRACK
CRACK CRACK
CRACK CRACK
CRACK CRACK
CRACK CRACK

CRACK!

© 1989 United Feature Syndicate, Inc.

ANOTHER YEAR, ANOTHER CRACK

JIM DAVIS

6-18

THE PRIMA BALLERNIA JETÉS ONTO THE STAGE

© 1989 United Feature Syndicate, Inc.      7-9

THE OLYMPIC GYMNAST FINISHES HIS ROUTINE WITH A FULL BACK LAYOUT

HERE WE ARE IN THE FINAL ROUND OF THE HOPSCOTCH COMPETITION

THE JACKHAMMER OPERATOR RIPS THROUGH 12 INCHES OF CONCRETE

OH, GARFIELD

JIM DAVIS

WHY CAN'T YOU JUST NUZZLE LIKE OTHER CATS?

YOU DESERVE BETTER

WORRIED ABOUT WRINKLES, GARFIELD?

JUST REMEMBER, WRINKLES ONLY EXIST TO SHOW WHERE THE SMILES HAVE BEEN

© 1989 United Feature Syndicate, Inc.

YOUR LIFE MUST BE A LAUGH RIOT

OH, SHUT UP

JIM DAVIS

7-28

Z

© 1989 United Feature Syndicate, Inc.

STOMP

ZINNNG!

HE DIDN'T EVEN SAY "GOODBYE"

JIM DAVIS

7-29

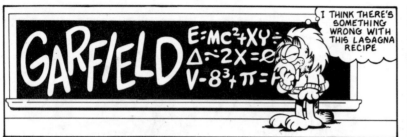

© 1989 United Feature Syndicate, Inc.

JIM DAVIS

9-3

# PROFESSOR GARFIELD'S
# NATURAL HISTORY OF DOGS

### PROTO-DOG
A BRAINLESS
SLIME DWELLER.

### DOGOSAUR
### 12 MILLION B.C.

HAD THE
MISFORTUNE
TO LIVE BEFORE
TREES AND FIRE
HYDRANTS HAD
EVOLVED;
SOON EXTINCT.

### CRO-MAGNON
### DOG
### 10,000 B.C.
DOMESTICATED
BUT STILL NOT
HOUSEBROKEN.

### WOOD-BURNING
### DOG
### CA. 1850
ANOTHER MISTAKE.

### MODERN DOG
AS YOU CAN SEE,
NOT A LOT OF
PROGRESS.